Winker WATSON

IT'S SNOWING!

SHUSH! I'M TRYING TO HEAR THIS...

DUE TO SUDDEN SNOWFALL, SCHOOLS ARE CLOSED UNTIL FURTHER NOTICE...

SNOW DAY!!

WOO!

YAY!

INTO CLASS, BOYS. DIDN'T YOU HEAR THE SCHOOL BELL?

BUT THE SCHOOLS ARE SHUT!

THAT'S FOR CHILDREN WHO CANNOT REACH SCHOOL THROUGH THE BLIZZARD, BUT YOU LOT ARE RESIDENTS HERE IN GREYTOWERS. NOW, INTO CLASS!

BAH! SNOWED INTO SCHOOL ON A SNOW DAY.

FEAR NOT, TROTTY. I SENSE A WANGLE-STORM APPROACHING. MEET ME IN THE COMPUTER ROOM AT BREAK.

AT BREAK TIME...

COMPUTER LAB

GRAB THOSE OFF THE PRINTER FOR ME, TROTTY. WE'RE ABOUT TO BECOME HEATING ENGINEERS!

PRINT-O-TRON

I'VE MADE NEW LABELS FOR THE THERMOSTAT. WE'LL TURN THE HEAT UP ON OL' CREEP BY TURNING IT DOWN IN THE SCHOOL!

Boiler Control

HOT---›COLD

HEATING CONTROLS DO NOT TOUCH!

CLEVER! THE CONTROLS ARE BACK TO FRONT NOW!

THERE, A NEW LABEL FOR THE RADIATOR, TOO. I'VE SWITCHED IT OFF, BUT IT LOOKS LIKE IT'S ON FULL BLAST!

HURRY UP, WINKER! CREEP'S COMING BACK!

BRRR! IT'S A BIT CHILLY IN HERE. TURN UP THE RADIATOR, TOMPKINS.

IT'S UP ALL THE WAY, SIR.

BERYL the PERIL

...AND HERE COMES BERYL AGAIN - SHE'S UNSTOPPABLE, THIS GIRL!

SHE BEATS ONE... BEATS TWO...

...AND SHOOTS!

WHUMP!

OH, MY WORD - WHAT A *SAVE!* INCREDIBLE!

WELL PLAYED, CYNTHIA!

THANK YOU! WHEEZE!

YOU'RE MY BESTIE, YOU ARE!

CAN WE PLAY SOMETHING ELSE, PLEASE?

SO...

DEMON SPINNER BERYL RUNS UP LIKE A COILED SPRING...

HURL!

...AND UNLEASHES THE PERFECT DELIVERY!

SO...

THIS IS...

...S-O-O-O BO-O-O-ORING!

SOON...

COME ON, CYNTHIA - DO SOMETHING!

ER, BERYL...

...IT'S YOUR MOVE.

WHAT? WHY DIDN'T YOU SAY SO?

I THOUGHT YOU KNEW.

NO, NO, NO, NO, NO! A BESTIE WOULD HAVE...

POUND! THUMP! THUD!

...SAID SOMETHING.

HOW DID THAT HAPPEN, CYNTH?

GRRRRRRRR!

UH-OH! MY BESTIE'S TURNED BEASTIE! SOMEONE NEEDS TO KEEP YOU IN CHECK, MATE!

BRIGHTY

Dandytown ADVENTURES! — MY FUNNY VALENTINE

IT'S VALENTINE'S DAY AND POSTMAN PRATT HAS A LOT TO DELIVER...

PHEW! I SHOULD GET PAID EXTRA ON DAYS LIKE THIS!

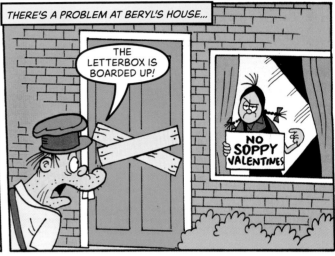

THERE'S A PROBLEM AT BERYL'S HOUSE...

THE LETTERBOX IS BOARDED UP!

NO SOPPY VALENTINES

PRATT WRITES A SIGN BACK...

I DON'T HAVE ANY CARDS FOR YOU.

WHY NOT? I'M LOVELY!

I JUST HAVE BILLS FOR YOUR DAD.

NO BILLS EITHER! GET LOST!

NOT A VERY GOOD START.

WHO'S NEXT?

IN THE GEORDIES' DEN...

HOWAY, LADS! WE'S GOT A HEART-SHAPED BOX AN' THAT, MAN!

IT'S FROM THE JOCKS AN' THAT!

FROM THE JOCKS

BLESS 'EM! I'M SURPRISED THEM JOCKS SPRUNG FOR THIS, LIKE!

FROM THE JOCKS

SPEAKING OF 'SPRUNG'...

BIFF!

AT CUDDLES AND DIMPLES' HOUSE...

THOSE BABIES OF OURS ARE AMAZING! THEY'VE SENT ME CHOCOLATES THROUGH THE POST!

ANYTHING FOR ME?

YES, HERE.

AWW! THEY LOVE ME AFTER ALL!

BUT...

URRGH! STINKY NAPPIES!

DARLING, CAN YOU TAKE YOUR GIFT OUTSIDE? IT'S PUTTING ME OFF MY CHOCOLATES.

THIS ONE'S FOR GREEDY PIGG! WHO LOVES GREEDY?!

UPON GETTING HIS VALENTINE, GREEDY QUICKLY OPENS IT...

CHOCOLATES!

WHO WOULD SEND GREEDY CHOCOLATES? - ED

THERE'S NOTHING THAT SAYS YOU CAN'T SEND A VALENTINE TO YOURSELF!

SCOFF! SCOFF!

AT THE ARMY BASE, COLONEL GRUMBLY GETS A CAKE DELIVERED...

EXPLAIN THIS, CLOTT!

I CAN'T! VALENTINES ARE MEANT TO BE HIPPOPOTAMUS!

WHAT?

HIPPOPOTAMUS? ANNOPOTOMUS? ANONYMOUS! YOU'RE NOT MEANT TO TELL!

YOU'RE NOT MEANT TO SEND A VALENTINE TO YOUR COMMANDING OFFICER!

SORRY, YOUR LORDSHIP, BUT EVER SINCE I CAME HERE YOU'VE BEEN LIKE A FATHER TO ME!

A GRUMPY FATHER.

SHUT UP! YOU'RE MAKING A VERY WEIRD SITUATION EVEN WEIRDER! I'LL JUST EAT IT.

IT'S JUST A NORMAL CAKE, RIGHT?

YES! I FOLLOWED THE RECIPE CAREFULLY.

I USED SUGAR, FLOUR, EGGS, COCOA POWDER, BAKING POWDER...

SUGAR   FLOUR   POWDERED EGGS   COACOA POWDER   GUN POWDER

IF THIS TASTES AS GOOD AS IT LOOKS, I'LL WANT A CAKE FROM YOU EVERY VALENTINE'S DAY!

THINKING ABOUT IT NOW, I MIGHT HAVE...

BOOM!

...OOPS!

WHAT DO YOU WANT FOR CHRISTMAS?

KORKY GETS A SMALL CARD...

I KNOW WHO THIS IS FROM, READERS. I GET ONE EVERY YEAR.

'TO KORKY, THANKS FOR NOT CATCHING US! ALL OUR LOVE, THE MICE.'

WE LOVE YOU, KORKY!

AT THE JOCKS' DEN...

HOOTS, MON! IT'S A VALENTINE AFF THON GEORDIES!

FROM THE GEORDIES

ARRGH!

IT HASNAE GAN BOOM!

GEE IT TIME!

WHAT CAN WE DAE?

NOWT!

WE CANNAE GO BACK NOO!

WE'LL HAVE TAE ABANDON THE DEN!

I'LL MISS THAT DEN AN AWFY LOT!

MEANWHILE, AT THE GEORDIES'...

I WISH WE HADN'T GOT THEM JOCKS CHOCS NOW!

BRASSNECK GETS WHAT HE ALWAYS WANTED...

A NEW OIL PUMP!

I THOUGHT YOU'D LIKE IT!

THE END.

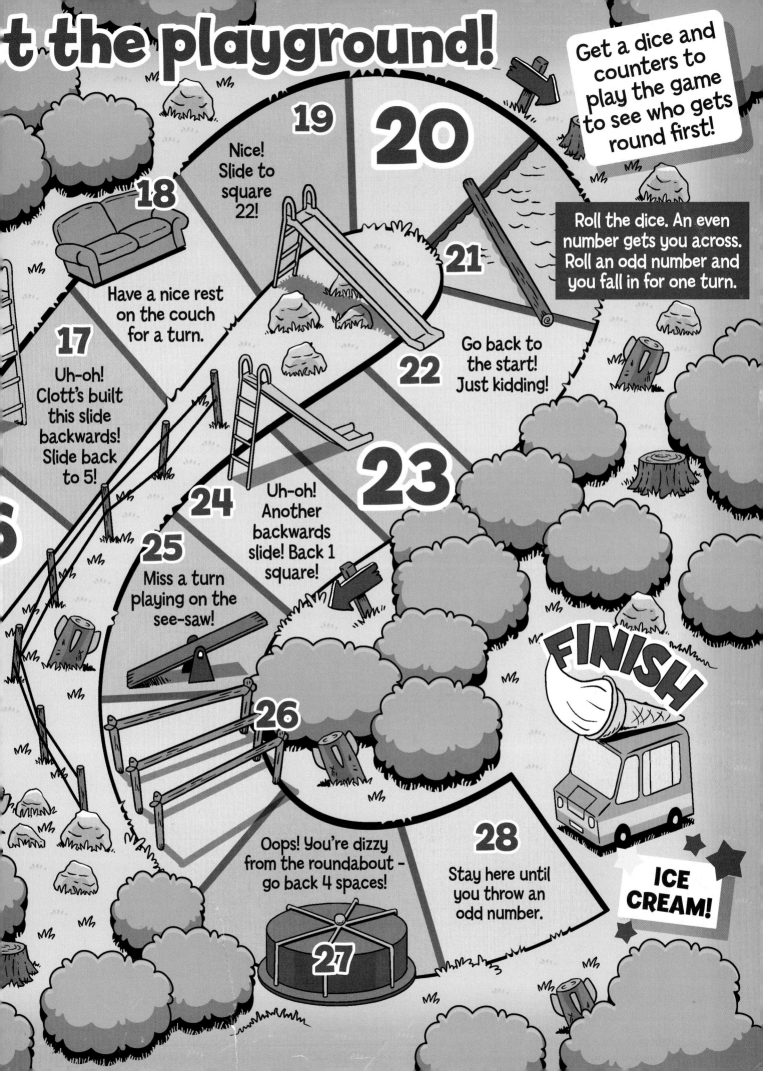

KORKY THE CAT

CUDDLES and DIMPLES

HEH-HEH. A LETTER DELIVERED WITHOUT CUDDLES AND DIMPLES SPOTTING ME. THAT COURSE THE S.A.S. DID FOR US POSTIES HAS PAID OFF.

ARRGH!

THE S.A.S. SHOULD KNOW US BETTER BY NOW.

THEY THE ONES WE CHASED WIV THE ALLIGATOR LAST WEEK?

THAT'S THEM. WHAT HAVE YOU GOT THERE, DEAR DADDY?

WHAT? NOTHING. I HAVE NOTHING. *NOT A THING.*

DIDN'T DADDY TELL US NOT TO TELL FIBS? I THINK HE'S FIBBING NOW.

FIBBERING IS BAD.

WHAT'S THIS? ANOTHER BILL.

NO, DON'T! IT'S...

A WEDDING INVITATION! OH NO.

OH YES! CAKE AND CHAOS - OUR FAVOURITE THINGS!

GET DRESSED. QUICKER YOU IS DRESSED, QUICKER WE CAUSE TROUBLE.

HE MEANS, THE QUICKER WE EAT CAKE.

Desperate Dan!

BERYL the PERIL

OFF TO WORK, FATHER?

YEP - ANOTHER DAY AT THE OFFICE FOR ME!

WHEN I GROW UP, I'M GOING TO BE JUST LIKE YOU, DAD!

AWWW... THAT'S NICE OF YOU TO SAY, BERYL.

I'M SURE YOU'LL DO VERY WELL AS A CORPORATE FINANCE ADVISOR.

THANK YOU.

SO, THAT'S WHAT HE DOES! I DON'T KNOW WHAT IT IS, BUT...

...IT SOUNDS REALLY BORING! FORGET THAT. I'LL THINK OF SOMETHING ELSE.

IT'S HARD DECIDING WHAT YOU WANT TO BE WHEN YOU GROW UP.

FLIP!

MAYBE I COULD BE A PROFESSIONAL FOOTBALLER?

BOOT!

CRASH!

OO-ER! OR MAYBE...

...A GLAZIER? HELLO, MR McGILL - I'M SURE I CAN FIX THAT FOR YOU!

SNORT!

MAYBE I COULD BE AN OLYMPIC RUNNER?

LEAP!

OR A HURDLER?

HOOK!

OOYAH! A CIRCUS CLOWN?

BLAT!

BACK HOME...

OR A DOCTOR, MAYBE?

OOYAH! YEOWCH! OR AN EVIL NURSE! THAT HURT!

RIPPP!

HMM... PERHAPS A CAREER AS A MAKE-UP ARTIST IS THE ROUTE I SHOULD GO?

KORKY THE CAT

YUM!

WHIMPER! THEY LOOK HUNGRY AND I THINK I'M ON THE MENU! SNIFF!

SLURP!

DRIBBLE!

SUDDENLY...

HAPPY EASTER!

UH-OH.

COME BACK, MR EASTER BUNNY! YOU DIDN'T GIVE ME A CHOCOLATE EGG!

WE LOVE RABBIT! YUM!

TIME I MADE AN EGGS-IT! HELP!

BANANAMAN

I NEED A BREAK FROM BEING A SUPERHERO.

I'LL GO BACK TO DANDYTOWN WHERE I USED TO LIVE. NOTHING BAD HAS HAPPENED THERE SINCE I LEFT.

TO DANDYTOWN

BUT HIDING IN DANDYTOWN...

GIVE ME A BREAK. WE CAME TO DANDYTOWN TO *GET AWAY* FROM THAT BIG, BLUE BOGEY.

WHY DOES HE HAVE TO RUIN EVERYTHING?!

BUT I HAVE A CUNNING PLAN TO FIX OLD BLUE-BLOOMERS.

DANDYTOWN CUSTOMS

STOP RIGHT THERE, SQUIRE.

MY NAME'S BANANAMAN, NOT SQUIRE.

UNLESS I'M SQUIRE BANANAMAN.

BUT I DON'T THINK SO - I CAN CHECK IF YOU LIKE?

LESS WITTERING, MORE DOING AS YOU'RE TOLD! LET'S SEE YOUR PASSPORT.

I DIDN'T KNOW I NEEDED A PASSPORT TO GET INTO DANDYTOWN.

IT'S IN MY POCKET.

BE A PAL AND HOLD THESE, WOULD YOU?

IT'S IN HERE SOMEWHERE.

WELL, EVERYTHING ELSE CERTAINLY IS!

I THINK I NEARLY HAVE IT.

YOU HAVEN'T GOT AN AMBULANCE IN THERE, HAVE YOU? I MAY NEED ONE.

THIS IS THE PLACE I NEED.

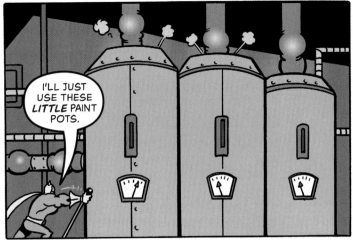

I'LL JUST USE THESE *LITTLE* PAINT POTS.

OOPS, WAS THAT ME? MY MISTAKE.

OOH! A RAINBOW - AND IT'S NOT EVEN RAINING!

AT GREYTOWERS SCHOOL...

SPLA-OOSH!

WHAT IN THE WORLD JUST HAPPENED?

I DON'T THINK WE CAN CALL IT *GREY*TOWERS ANY MORE.

HA-HA!

LESS LAUGHING - YOU'RE CLEANING IT ALL OFF.

SUDDENLY IT'S NOT SO FUNNY.

WELL, *I'M* LAUGHING.

STOP BEING SO ROTTEN.

I'M BEING TOLD OFF BY A TALKING CAT. I STILL HAVE SOME PAINT LEFT.

A SPLISH HERE, A SPLASH THERE, NOW YOU'RE A...

I'LL JUST CLIMB UP HERE AND SEE IF I CAN SEE...

...DAN! FANCY MEETING YOU HERE.

I CAN'T HELP BEIN' HERE WHEN YOU'RE CLIMBING MY LEGS! WHAT BRINGS YOU HERE?

OF COURSE I'LL HELP. I GOT NO PLANS TILL SUPPER TIME ANYWAYS.

BRILLIANT, MR SHRIEK, TAKE US HOME!

YOU COULD MAKE A FORTUNE BY REPLACING THE BUSES.

ALL MY CENTURIES OF EVIL TRAINING AND I'M A TAXI!

LISTEN UP, BANANA-BUDDY. I HEAR YOU'VE BEEN CAUSING TROUBLE, WELL, I THINK YOU NEEDS TO STOP.

DO YOU?

LET ME THINK ABOUT THAT...

...NO!

RASSP!

IF I DIDN'T KNOW BETTER I'D SAY THIS FELLER IS JUST BEING RUDE.

HE REALLY IS.

WELL, I JUST CAN'T ABIDE RUDE.

GNNNNG!

MY AUNT AGGIE TAUGHT ME TO HAVE GOOD MANNERS.

THE STAR OF THE SHOW STEPS OUT AND OPENS HIS MOUTH...

I THINK I PROBABLY SHOULD HAVE THOUGHT OF SOMETHING TO SING BEFORE I CAME OUT HERE!

THIS IS HOW ENTERTAINED THE TROOPS ARE...

JUST SING ANYTHING!

DON'T SHOUT, MR GRUMBLY! YOU'RE ALWAYS SHOUTING! YOU'RE LIKE THIS - 'BLAH, BLAH, BLAH! I'M CROSS! I NEED A NAP!'

HA HA HA

HA HA HA

GRUMBLY REALISES THE TROOPS ARE ENTERTAINED BY CLOTT'S IMPRESSIONS...

KEEP GOING!

HA HA HA   HA HA HA HA

I'M COLONEL GRUMBLYPANTS AND I'VE GOT A STINKY BUTT!

HEY!

HA HA HA HA HA

ON A ROLL, CLOTT TRIES TO PULL THE MICROPHONE OUT OF THE STAND...

URRGH!

IS THIS THING GLUED ON?!

PULL! PULL!

CLONK!

POP!

COMEDY GENIUS!

HA-HA!

THE NEXT MORNING AT THE BASE'S INFIRMARY...

YOU WERE A HUGE HIT! CAN YOU CALL ME A STINK BUTT THEN KNOCK YOURSELF OUT EVERY FRIDAY?

WHAT HAPPENED?

YES, I CAN!

Winker WATSON

WHAT A LOVELY DAY! SHAME WE HAVE TO SPEND IT INDOORS DOING BORING LESSONS.

MAYBE I CAN COME UP WITH A WANGLE TO...

IT'S TOO NICE A DAY TO SPEND INDOORS, EH, LADS? WHAT DO YOU SAY WE TAKE OUR LESSONS OUTSIDE?

...GET US OUTSIDE, WHAT?

WOO-HOO!

THIS SEEMS A BIT FISHY TO ME.

OH, THIS WILL NEVER DO. WE'LL HAVE TO GET THIS PLACE TIDIED UP BEFORE WE CAN GET ANY SCHOOLING DONE.

AH! MR HEADMASTER! WHAT A COINCIDENCE! I WAS JUST SAYING TO THE BOYS HERE THAT THE GROUNDS COULD DO WITH A BIT OF A SPRING CLEAN.

HOW VERY FORTUNATE INDEED, MR CREEP, THAT I WAS JUST PASSING THIS VERY SPOT WITH ALL OF THESE TOOLS.

THIS IS ROTTEN! YOU TRICKED US!

I THOUGHT GREYTOWERS HAD A GROUNDSKEEPER? WHAT'S HAPPENED TO HIM?

OUR BUDGET WAS VERY TIGHT THIS YEAR. WE HAD SOME VERY TOUGH DECISIONS TO MAKE.

GREYTOWERS
ANNUAL
BUDGET
GROUNDSKEEPER X
STAFF ROOM
BISCUIT SUPPLY ✓

I THINK WE MADE THE RIGHT DECISION, MUNCH!

OKAY! TOOL UP AND GET TO WORK, BOYS!

I THINK I'D RATHER BE IN CLASS.

CLANG!

HELLO? WHAT'S THIS?

THIS MUST HAVE BEEN LEFT BEHIND BY BUILDERS YEARS AGO!

I CAN FEEL A WANGLE FROM ANCIENT HISTORY COMING ON!

HELP ME WITH THIS LOT.

SAND

Greytowers Treasure Hunt!

CAN YOU FIND THE TEN GENUINE LOST TREASURES CONCEALED IN GREYTOWERS' OVERGROWN GARDENS?

TICK 'EM OFF AS YOU FIND THEM!

- ☐ MINT CONDITION COPY OF DANDY NO.1
- ☐ BLACKBEARD'S TREASURE
- ☐ THE 'BARK' OF THE COVENANT
- ☐ 'WRANGLER WITH APPLE' – A PAINTING BY JOHANNES VAN HOYTL THE YOUNGER (1613-1669)
- ☐ BLACKBEARD'S LUNCH
- ☐ FOSSILISED SKULL OF A RARE CLOWNOSAURUS
- ☐ NEST OF THE VERY RARE FLIGHTLESS WANGLETHRIP
- ☐ A METEORITE WITH AN INTERPLANETARY PASSENGER
- ☐ A SAXON BISCUIT HOARD
- ☐ THE ORIGINAL WORLD CUP TROPHY

SOLUTION

NICK BRENNAN

KATE AND HER PARENTS ARE VISITING AN OLD CASTLE...

THIS CASTLE HAS A RATHER FASCINATING HISTORY.

BAH! THIS IS NOT THE WAY I WANTED TO SPEND THE SCHOOL HOLIDAYS!

HMM, I SUPPOSE YOU'D RATHER BE PEEKING THROUGH KEYHOLES?

EVERYONE NEEDS A HOBBY, DAD!

HERE WE HAVE A LOVELY EXAMPLE OF A DOOR MADE OF SOLID OAK!

FORGET THE DOOR! LOOK AT THAT KEYHOLE! WOW!

SIGH. HERE WE GO!

ANCIENT SUIT OF ARMOUR

NEVER MIND THAT! WE'RE GOING TO LOSE THE TOUR GUIDE!

LEGEND HAS IT THAT THIS CASTLE IS HAUNTED, BUT I DON'T THINK WE NEED TO WORRY ABOUT SILLY GHOST STORIES!

HA-HA!

AS IF!

I CAN'T RESIST JUST ONE LITTLE PEEK THROUGH THAT ANCIENT KEYHOLE!

LET'S SEE WHAT... EEK!

HELLO!

ARRGH! SPIDER! WHOA!

CLATTER!

YIKES!

WHAT'S ALL THE NOISE BACK HERE? YIKES!

EEK! THE GHOST! RUN!

SHRIEK! WE'LL NEVER VISIT THIS PLACE AGAIN!

RELAX! IT'S ONLY ME!

TOO LATE! THEY'VE ALL RUN OFF NOW!

GRR! YOU'RE BANNED!

SIGH! WE SHOULD HAVE KNOWN WE HADN'T A GHOST OF A CHANCE KEEPING KATE AWAY FROM A KEYHOLE-RELATED DISASTER!

HEE-HEE!

AND THIS IS THE HOT TUB.

I THINK I'M GONNA BE SICK!

WE'VE ALSO GOT THE 24 HOUR VAMPIRE CHANNEL! YOU'LL LOVE IT!

THE VAMPIRE CHANNEL

CLICK!

I'LL LEAVE YOU TO YOUR SLUMBERS, HAPPY NIGHTMARES, SIR! CACKLE!

I DON'T WANT TO WATCH THIS STUFF!

CLICK!
CLICK!
CLICK!
CLICK!
CLICK!
CLICK!
CLICK!

SO...

I'M A HAPPY, HAPPY, HAPPY, HAPPY, HAPPY BUNNY!

THE FLUFFY PINK BUNNIES STATION! MY FAVE!

CLAP!

I NEED TO TURN UP THE VOLUME TO DROWN OUT ALL THOSE SCARY NOISES FROM THE FLOOR BELOW.

ARRGH!
CACKLE!
ROAR!
CLANG!
GROAN!
MOAN!
RATTLE!
SCREAM!

TRA LA LA! SING ALONG KIDS!

HA! HA! HA! LITTLE BUNNIES!

THE NEXT MORNING...

MASTER 'ERBERT, WE'VE HAD NUMEROUS COMPLAINTS ABOUT THE LOUD HAPPY MUSIC YOU WERE PLAYING LAST NIGHT. IF I GIVE YOU THIS, WILL YOU PLEASE LEAVE?

TONI CREEP

A fab free holiday for two at Happy Land.

Sun, fun, games, singing, dancing, kids' treats, lovely grub! No rain!

GOSH! YES, PLEASE!

MUTTER, I WAS HAVING FUN! GRUMBLE!

I'M A HAPPY, HAPPY, HAPPY, HAPPY LITTLE BUNNY!

FIZZY POP

ADMIT 2

KORKY THE CAT

Winker WATSON

DOESN'T GREYTOWERS HAVE A POOL?

YEAH, BUT WE HAVEN'T USED IT IN *AGES!*

YIKES! NO WONDER WE NEVER USE IT!

MAYBE WE CAN CLEAR SOME OF THIS OUT.

I DON'T THINK SO, WINKER. WHATEVER IS IN THIS POOL IS NOT WATER ANY MORE!

HAS ANYONE SEEN WATKINS? I SWEAR HE WAS BESIDE ME A SECOND AGO.

I CAN'T BELIEVE THE STATE OF THAT POOL!

MY MUM WORKS THREE JOBS SO SHE CAN AFFORD TO SEND ME HERE! WHERE'S ALL THAT MONEY GOING?

WHAT WAS THAT, LADS? I CAN'T HEAR YOU OVER THE SOUND OF HOW AWESOME MY NEW CAR IS!

A NEW SPORTS CAR?! WAIT! ARE YOU CLEANING IT WITH BOTTLED WATER IN THE MIDDLE OF A HEATWAVE?

EAU SO FANCY Mineral Water 1 Doz.

HED 1

CAN WE HAVE SOME OF THAT WATER, SIR? WE'RE PARCHED!

CERTAINLY NOT! THE CAR NEEDS IT. SHE'S GOT SENSITIVE PAINTWORK! ONLY NATURE'S BEST!

EAU SO FANCY

NATURE! THAT'S IT! FORGET THE BOTTLED WATER, LET'S HIT THE RIVER, LADS!

GREAT IDEA!

THIS'LL COOL US OFF!

RIVER

DIVE BOMB!

LEAP!

OOF!

WHERE'S THE WATER GONE? WHERE'S OUR RIVER?

Desperate Dan!

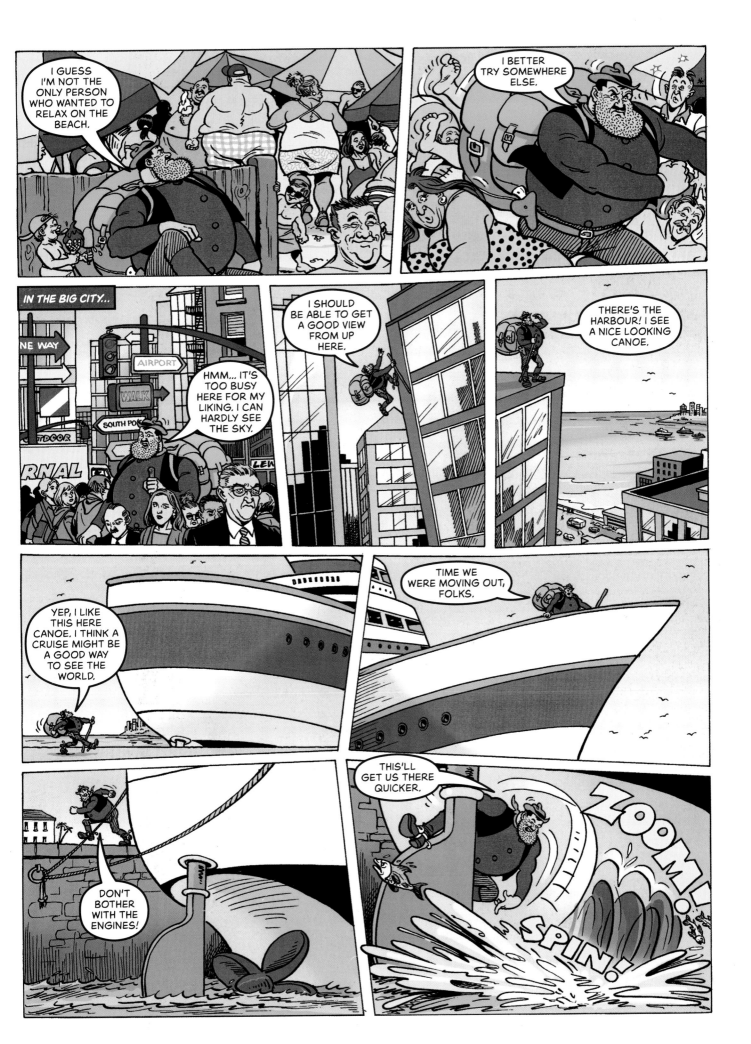

Wish he WASN'T here!

DAN'S HOLIDAY HAS TAKEN HIM ALL AROUND THE WORLD... AND THE WORLD WISHES HE HAD STAYED AT HOME. HE SENT US SOME OF HIS HOLIDAY PICTURES. CAN YOU FILL IN THE NAMES OF THE PLACES HE VISITED?

2

E_____

A_____

4

I_____

3

G_____ B_____

5

C_____

SOME KIDS HAVE DADS WHO...

...ARE TALLER THAN EVERYONE ELSE'S.

WHILST OTHER KIDS HAVE DADS WHO ARE STRONGER THAN ANYONE ELSE'S.

THEN THERE ARE THE KIDS WHOSE DADS ARE JUST CLEVERER THAN ANYONE ELSE'S.

MY DAD...

...MY DAD GROWS BIG VEGETABLES,

MARROWS TO BE PRECISE! FOR THE ANNUAL VEGETABLE SHOW!

MY MARROW IS BIGGER THAN ANY OTHER DAD'S AND IT'S GOING TO WIN TODAY'S DANDYTOWN SHOW PRIZE!

THAT'S MY DAD... EVER HOPEFUL!

MORNING, BERYL. HELLO, SON.

HIYA, GRANDAD!

HELLO, DAD - WHERE ARE YOU OFF TO?

SOLUTION: RE ARE 11 FAKE CUDDLES(RED) AND 10 FAKE DIMPLES (BLUE). REAL CUDDLES AND DIMPLES ARE SCOFFING CHOCOLATES!

KEYHOLE KATE

KATE HAS BEEN HELPING HER DAD CLEAR OUT THE SHED...

≧COUGH!≧ IT'S SO DUSTY IN HERE! I NEED TO TAKE A BREAK!

I'LL JUST LOOK THROUGH A FEW MORE THINGS!

WOW! THIS OLD BOX LOOKS ANCIENT! I WONDER WHAT'S INSIDE?

I'LL JUST CLEAR THE COBWEBS FROM THE LOCK AND...

...WHOA! WHO ARE YOU?

PWUFF!

I AM THE GENIE OF THE SHED, AND I GRANT YOU THREE WISHES!

BRILLIANT! I'M OBSESSED WITH KEYHOLES SO I WISH EVERY DOOR IN THE HOUSE HAD A GREAT BIG KEYHOLE IN IT!

YOUR WISH IS GRANTED!

OOPS! THESE KEYHOLES ARE A BIT BIGGER THAN I EXPECTED!

SHRIEK! BATHROOM

YIKES! SORRY, DAD! I DIDN'T REALISE YOU MEANT THAT SORT OF BREAK!

SECOND WISH,— I WISH I HAD ALL THE KEYHOLES IN THE WORLD!

YOUR WISH WILL BE GRANTED!

YEEK! I DIDN'T KNOW THERE'D BE QUITE THIS MANY!

CLATTER! CLUNK!

KEYHOLE KATE, I'M ARRESTING YOU FOR NICKING ALL THE KEYHOLES IN THE WORLD!

NOOO! IT'S ALL GONE PEAR-SHAPED! I WISH I WAS BACK AT THE START OF THIS STORY!

YOUR FINAL WISH IS MY COMMAND! GOODBYE!

I'VE GONE BACK IN TIME! PERFECT!

THROWING THAT BOX OUT WITHOUT PEEKING THROUGH THE KEYHOLE? THAT'S NOT LIKE YOU, KATE!

BELIEVE ME, DAD, IT WOULD LEAD TO A HOLE LOT OF TROUBLE! SIGH!

LEW STRINGER

Desperate Dan!

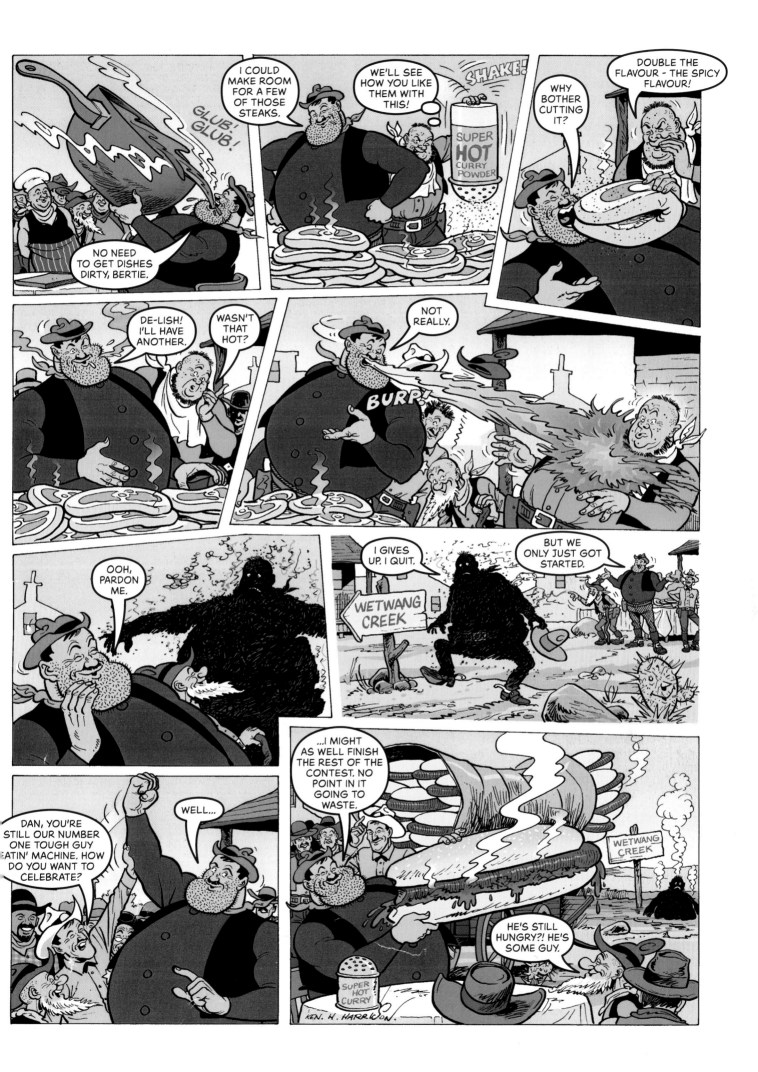

KORKY THE CAT

IT'S HALLOWEEN...

TIME TO GO TRICK OR TREATING. I MUSTN'T FORGET MY COSTUME.

TRICK OR TREAT?

OH MY! WHAT A SCARY LOOKING GHOST, HA-HA!

HERE YOU ARE, HAPPY HALLOWEEN!

THANK YOU!

BAH! ALL I GOT WAS SWEETS!

AT THE NEXT HOUSE...

HERE YOU GO. THESE TREATS SHOULD LIFT YOUR SPIRITS, HA!

MANY HOUSES LATER...

ARRGH! MORE SWEETS! WHERE ARE THE TREATS?!

SHH!

DANDYTOWN FISH CLUB NIGHT FISHING NIGHT

KEEP THE NOISE DOWN! I'M TRYING TO FISH HERE, STUPID CAT!

PURR-FECT! BUT I NEED TO GET A SCARIER COSTUME IF I STAND A GHOST'S CHANCE OF GETTING MY TREAT.

HEY, KID, SWAP YOU MY COSTUME AND THIS BAG OF SWEETS FOR YOUR VAMPIRE TEETH AND CAPE.

WOW! ARE YOU FUR-REAL?

SO...

BOO! I'M LOOKING FOR A QUICK BITE!

ARRGH! VAMPIRE CAT!

YUM! A TRICK FOLLOWED BY A BOO-TIFUL TREAT.

HUNT EMERSON

THAT'S THE WORM ON THE HOOK, TROTTY.

AND CREEPY REALLY IS A WORM.

IN DRAMA CLUB AT BREAK...

ARE YOU READY FOR YOUR BEST PERFORMANCE EVER, JAKE?

READY, WINKER!

WHO WOULD PHONE AT BREAK TIME?! I'M TRYING TO HAVE A CUP OF TEA.

BRRING!

HELLO? IS THAT THE HEADMASTER OF GREYTOWERS SCHOOL? I'M THE LEADER OF THE BRITISH ASTRONOMY AND METEOR SOCIETY.

HOW CAN I HELP?

THE BEST VIEW IN THE WORLD OF TONIGHT'S METEOR SHOWER IS FROM YOUR SCHOOL.

AND?

WE'D LIKE TO PAY YOU CASH TO WATCH THE METEORS FROM YOUR SCHOOL. SHALL WE SAY A THOUSAND POUNDS?

CASH? THAT'S MY FAVOURITE KIND OF MONEY!

OF COURSE! WE'D BE HAPPY TO HAVE YOUR LOVELY PEOPLE HERE AND TO TAKE YOUR LOVELY MONEY.

MONEY, MR CREEP, MONEY! BUY MORE BISCUITS! BUY CAKE! WE'RE RICH!

CAKE? WHAT A GREAT DAY!

WE HAVE TO LOOK OUR BEST, MR CREEP.

AT LEAST UNTIL THEY HAND OVER THE DOSH.

YOU BOYS GO AND STUDY IN YOUR ROOMS OR SOMETHING. I'M TOO BUSY TO TEACH YOU.

IF YOU SAY SO, SIR.

YOU'VE GOT US AN AFTERNOON OFF, WINKER, BUT HOW DOES THIS GET US A FIREWORKS SHOW?

TRUST ME, TROTTY. IT'S ALL IN HAND.

THAT'S IT DONE, WINKER. THIS MICROPHONE IS HOOKED INTO ALL THE DIGITAL RADIOS IN SCHOOL - INCLUDING THE HEAD'S AND OLD CREEPY'S.

GOOD WORK.

HERE IS THE LATEST WEATHER REPORT...

...HIGH CLOUD TONIGHT WILL BLOCK OUT ANY VIEW OF THE METEOR SHOWER.

I HOPE THAT ASTRONOMY CHAP DIDN'T HEAR THAT.

WHIMPER!

DRRING!

I JUST HEARD ON THE RADIO ABOUT CLOUDS TONIGHT. WE'D BETTER CANCEL THE VISIT.

NO, NO, DON'T CANCEL. THE SKY WILL BE CLEAR HERE TONIGHT. REALLY, THEY WILL.

NO! THEY'VE CANCELLED!

BUT WE'VE ALREADY SPENT THE CASH!

CAKE

BOXSTATION 4

FANCY BISCUITS

FLAT SCREEN TV

EVEN FANCIER BISCUITS

I HOPE WE SEE THE METEOR SHOWER TONIGHT, TROTTY. THEY LOOK EXACTLY LIKE FIREWORKS GOING OFF.

< LIBRARY

STAFF LOUNGE

THEY DO?

IS THAT THE FIREWORKS SHOP? I DON'T CARE HOW MUCH IT COSTS, I NEED A DISPLAY AT GREYTOWERS SCHOOL TONIGHT!

THEY'D BETTER TURN UP SOON, MR CREEP, OR THEY'LL MISS THE FIREWORKS... I MEAN 'METEOR SHOWER'.

AND THEY HAVEN'T GIVEN US THE CASH YET.

THIS IS YOUR BRIGHTEST SCAM YET.

THERE WILL BE EVEN MORE FIREWORKS WHEN THE ASTRONOMERS DON'T TURN UP.

ALAN RYAN!

POW! POW! HIGH SCORE!

THAT'S ENOUGH GAMING, BLINKY.

IT'S TIME TO DECORATE THE TREE.

WOO-HOO!

THIS IS THE BEST TREE EVER!

FUME!

GRRR...

EEK! EVERGREEN ATTACK!

PERHAPS IT'S BEST IF YOU PLAY OUTSIDE IN THE SNOW.

BOOT!

FLUP!

I'LL GO SLEDGING! NOW, WHERE'S MY SLEDGE?

DOG

YOU HAVEN'T GOT ONE, YOU NINCOMPOOP.

AH, HERE IT IS!

RIP!

SIGH.

NOW TO FIND A HILL.

OOF! STEEP!

NICK BRENNAN

MEANWHILE...

FINISHED! I'LL CALL BLINKY IN TO SEE IT.

BLINKY! COME AND SEE THE TREE!

HERE I COME! WHEEEEE!

RUMBLE!

FLUMP!

BRRRR!

WOWSERS! WHAT A TREE!

IT JUST NEEDS ONE MORE THING...

FLUP!

A FAIRY ON THE TOP! PERFECT!

LATER...

ATCHOO! BLART!

TAP! TAP!

I'VE CAUGHT A COLD FROM BEING BURIED IN THE SNOW!

I WON'T BE ABLE TO COOK CHRISTMAS DINNER LIKE THIS.

DON'T WORRY, MOTHER...

...I'LL TAKE CARE OF EVERYTHING!

THAT'S WHAT I AM WORRIED ABOUT!

I'LL SORT THE BIRD FIRST.

POP IT IN THE OVEN...

SHOVE!

...AND THREE HOURS ON FULL.

CLICK-CLICK!

NOW FOR THE VEG.

MOTHER SAYS SPROUTS ARE GOOD FOR YOU.

PONG!

SO I'VE DONE PLENTY. I LOVE THEM!

HE REALLY IS BONKERS!

SPROUTS

PIGS IN BLANKETS NEXT.

CHOMP! CHOMP!

RECIPE Book

HMMM... I'M SURE I PUT THE SAUSAGES DOWN HERE.

BEEP! BEEP!

TURKEY'S READY!

MMMMM... DONE TO A TURN!

SLOOSH!

I'LL BRING YOU CHRISTMAS DINNER IN BED!

I'VE GOT CRACKERS AS WELL, MOTHER!

HE CERTAINLY IS THAT!

NICK BRENNAN

A very Dandy Christmas!

'TWAS THE NIGHT BEFORE CHRISTMAS...

GRRRRR!

...WHEN ALL THROUGH THE HOUSE NOT A CREATURE WAS STIRRING, NOT EVEN A MOUSE!

STOP THAT!

SORRY, KORKY!

THE STOCKINGS WERE HUNG BY THE CHIMNEY WITH CARE...

BERYL

...IN THE HOPES THAT THE LATEST GAMES CONSOLES AND VR EQUIPMENT SOON WOULD BE THERE.

THE CHILDREN WERE NESTLED ALL SNUG IN THEIR BEDS. WHILE VISIONS OF SUGAR BOMBS DANCED IN THEIR HEADS.

THAT'S THE LAST TIME WE'RE GETTING THIS CEREAL!

BOUNCE!

BOUNCE!

SUGAR BOMBS

I IN MY CAP HAD JUST SETTLED IN FOR A LONG WINTER'S NAP...

CRASH!

...WHEN OUT ON THE LAWN THERE AROSE SUCH A CLATTER...

...I RAN TO THE WINDOW TO SEE WHAT WAS THE MATTER.

DO YOU KNOW WHAT TIME IT IS?!

SORRY! BLINKY WAS DRIVING!

WHEN TO MY WANDERING EYE WHO SHOULD APPEAR, BUT A BIG JOLLY MAN AND HIS ONE MAGIC REINDEER!

STEADY! HOW DO YOU LAND THIS THING?!

MOO!

IT'S ME, READERS! DAN!

THE REAL SANTA COULDN'T DO THIS. HE'S TOO BUSY GETTING READY FOR CHRISTMAS!

MOO!

I THINK THE COWBOY HAT MAY HAVE GIVEN IT AWAY!

NOW, SMASHER! NOW, DINAH! NOW, WINKER AND THICK HEAD! NOW, BIG HEAD! NOW, CLOTT! ON, DIMPLES AND BRASSNECK!

NOW WHAT?

ON WHERE?

SO UP TO THE HOUSETOP THE REINDEER FLEW, WITH A SLEIGH FULL OF TOYS AND SANTA TOO!

CAREFUL!

MOO!

THEN IN A TWINKLING I HEARD ON THE ROOF, THE PRANCING AND PAWING OF EACH TINY HOOF!

CRASH! CLATTER! CRACK! SMASH!

OOPS!

TINY HOOF?!

CORPORAL CLOTT

THE POINT OF CAMOUFLAGE IS TO BLEND IN, TO NOT BE SEEN!

BUT IT'S CHRISTMAS!

LOOK WHAT YOU DID TO MY BEAUTIFUL GUARD TOWER!

I MADE IT MORE BEAUTIFUL!

WELL, I HATE IT! IT MIGHT BE CHRISTMAS BUT IT'S NOT ARMY REGULATION!

I DECORATED YOUR GROTTO TOO!

SPILL!

IT'S CALLED AN OFFICE!

GET RID OF IT ALL! THE ARMY IS NO PLACE FOR CHRISTMAS!

WAAAAAH!

?

WHAT?

LOOK INSIDE YOUR GROTTO.

IT'S AN OFFICE!

Desperate Dan!

IT'S REAL CLOSE TO CHRISTMAS, NEPHEW.

IT SURE IS, AUNT AGGIE.

BUT IT DOESN'T FEEL LIKE CHRISTMAS WITH THIS HOT WEATHER. PEOPLE ARE SAYING THEY CAN'T GET INTO THE CHRISTMAS SPIRIT.

THAT SURE IS SAD.

WAFT!

CALENDAR

I'M GONNA FIX THIS RIGHT NOW, AUNT AGGIE!

BUT I'M NOT SURE HOW - IT *REALLY* AIN'T CHRISTMASSY OUT HERE.

PI SHOP

BOOTS & SPURS

BEANZ

HATS

CH

GASP!

HOWDY, MA'AM, DON'T MIND ME.

I'M JUST BORROWING THIS, I'LL BRING IT BACK AFTER CHRISTMAS.

RRRIP!

SLAM!

NOW WE GOT US A TREE.

NOT TO MENTION SOME BIG OL' CRACKS IN THE GROUND.